Foreword

This series of books provides teachers with a wide variety of activities which will give their pupils the opportunity to develop an awareness of the important episodes and developments in ancient civilisations and a chronological framework.

The materials in **Ancient Greece and Egypt** can be used to support a whole class theme, by groups or by individual pupils for their research.

The activities cover all the detail of the Study Unit and develop the Key Elements.

Contents

ℕational Curriculum Reference Chart

Page Title	Pg	Key Elements											
		1a	1b	2a	2b	2c	3a	4a	4b	4c	5a	5b	5c
Ancient Greece	1							•	•	•	•	•	
Ancient Greece Timeline	2	•						•	•	•	•	•	
Life in Ancient Greece	3			•				•	•	•		•	
Greek 'Who's Who'	4			•				•	•	•		•	
Working People in Greece	5					•		•	•	•		•	
Ancient Greek Houses	6			•				•	•	•		•	
Famous Sites in Greece	7			•				•	•	•		•	
The Parthenon	8	•						•	•	•	•	•	
The People Who Worked on the Parthenon	9							•	•	•		•	
Greek Writing	10			•				•	•	•		•	
Greek Words	11			•				•	•	•		•	
The Olympic Games	12					•		•	•	•		•	
Greek Gods and Goddesses	13			•				•	•	•		•	
The Story of the Seasons	14			•				•	•	•		•	
Greek Heroes	15			•				•	•	•		•	
Greek Artefacts	16							•	•	•		•	
Ancient Egypt	17							•	•	•	•	•	
Ancient Egypt Timeline	18	•						•	•	•	•	•	
Powerful People	19			•				•	•	•		•	
Working People in Egypt	20			•				•	•	•		•	
Famous Sites in Egypt	21			•				•	•	•		•	
Egyptian Writing	22		•	•				•	•	•		•	
Entertainment	23			•				•	•	•		•	
Farming and Hunting	24			•				•	•	•		•	
Food	25			•				•	•	•		•	
Egyptian Gods and Goddesses	26			•				•	•	•		•	
Mummification	27			•				•	•	•		•	
Pharoh's Life After Death	28			•				•	•	•		•	
Egyptian Artefacts	29							•	•	•		•	
Word Grid	30		•					•	•	•		•	

ncient Greece

Can you put these labels in the correct place on the map?

| Sparta | Troy | Athens | Marathon | Olympia | Mycenae |

Shade the seas blue. Shade the coastlines green.
Most of Greece is mountainous, can you show this on the map?

ⒶΝCIENT Greece Τimeline

Can you match the dates to the pictures?
Cut them out and put them into date order on a timeline.

146 BC - Rome conquers Greece

490 BC - The Battle of Marathon

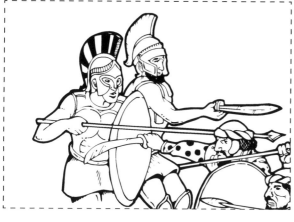

1250 BC - Fall of Troy

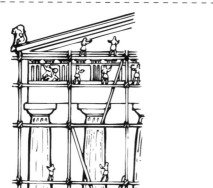

338 BC - Philip II becomes first King of Greece

431-414 BC - War between Athens and Sparta

433 BC - The Parthenon is completed

Life in Ancient Greece

Before Greece was united it was made up of separate 'city-states'. Each city-state was different, had different laws and lived differently. Two of the most famous city-states were Athens and Sparta.

Athens was a democracy, which means it was governed by the people and the people had a lot of freedom.

Sparta was different to most other city-states. It was harsh and severe, all of the men were soldiers.

Look at these facts.

Can you decide if they describe Athens or Sparta?

Put an 'A' for Athens or a 'S' for Sparta in the correct box.

☐ The girls stayed at home and learnt to weave.

☐ The girls went to the gymnasium and played sports.

☐ There was a full time army.

☐ There was an army in times of war.

☐ The kings and the important men made the decisions.

☐ The people made the decisions.

☐ The houses and public buildings were small and plain.

☐ The houses and public buildings were beautiful.

☐ There were famous playwrights and scientists.

☐ There were no plays, only some music.

☐ The people had a lot of freedom.

☐ The people had to do as they were told most of the time.

greek 'Who's Who'

Match these people who lived in Ancient Greece to what they did.

Archimedes

Pythagorus

Socrates

Sophocles

Sappho

Aristotle

Homer

He was a philosopher and thinker. He started his own school.

She was a writer and a poet. She came from the island of Lesbos.

He was the author of the 'Illiad' and the 'Odyssey'. These told old Greek stories.

He was a mathematician. He worked out many theorems we use today.

He was the most famous playwright and dramatist in Ancient Greece.

He was a philosopher and thinker who has influenced us today.

He was a scientist. Among other things he worked out the displacement of water theory.

Can you find out when each of these people lived?

*W*orking *P*eople in *G*reece

Look at these illustrations of people working in Ancient Greece.
Beside each one draw a picture of someone doing the same job today.

Ancient Greek Houses

Look at this illustration of a Ancient Greek house.

Can you label these places?

Bedrooms	Entrance	Inner courtyard
Living room	Kitchen	Storage courtyard
Dining room	Family alter	Women's room

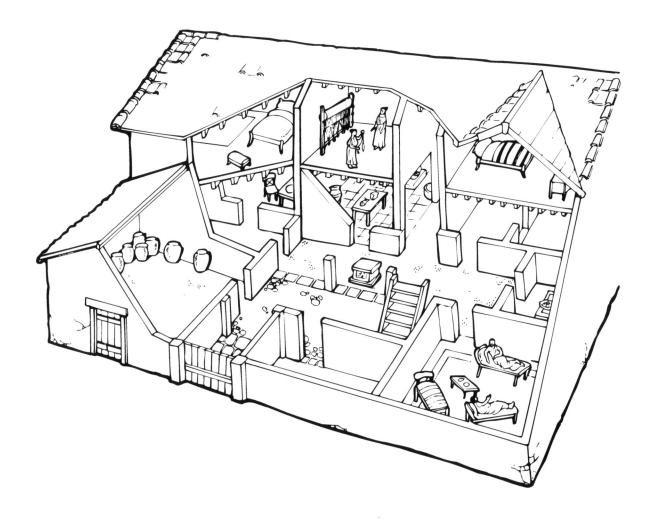

Famous Sites in Greece

There are many famous sites which have survived since the time of Ancient Greece.

Can you name these different sorts of buildings?

The _____

This building was made of stone and marble. It was built on the Acropolis.

The _____ _____

These were part of the decorations taken from the Parthenon.

A _____

These were used for sports, games and competitions. There is one surviving at Delphi.

An _____

This was used for plays and concerts. The seats were often built into the hillside.

The Parthenon

This was a great temple built in honour of the goddess Athene. Some of it is still standing on the Acropolis in Athens. It was a great building.

Look at these pictures which tell how it was built.
Can you put them in the correct order?

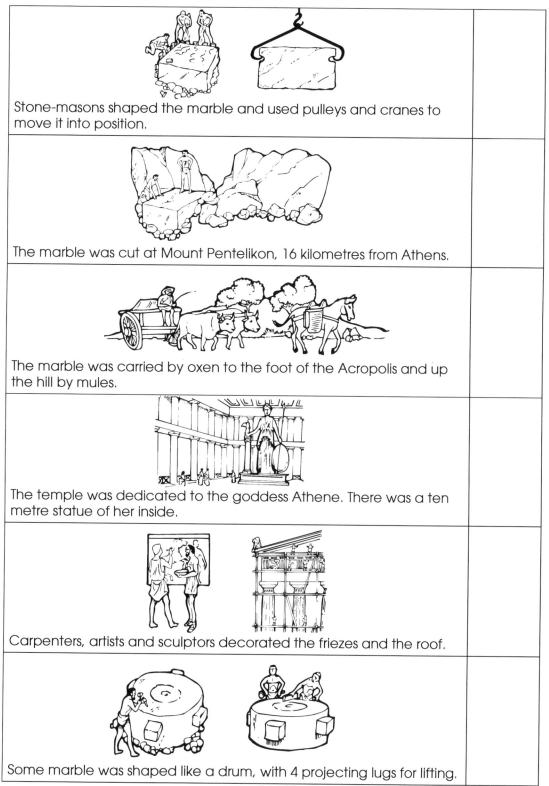

Stone-masons shaped the marble and used pulleys and cranes to move it into position.	
The marble was cut at Mount Pentelikon, 16 kilometres from Athens.	
The marble was carried by oxen to the foot of the Acropolis and up the hill by mules.	
The temple was dedicated to the goddess Athene. There was a ten metre statue of her inside.	
Carpenters, artists and sculptors decorated the friezes and the roof.	
Some marble was shaped like a drum, with 4 projecting lugs for lifting.	

The People Who Worked on the Parthenon

Here are some of the jobs people did during the building and furnishing of the Parthenon.

Sculptor
Making the statue of Athene and the other statues for the temple.

Carpenter
Making hoists, beams and scaffolding for the building.

Stonemason
Carving the white marble to make columns and blocks.

Roadbuilder
Making the roads for the men, mules and oxen to carry the marble and other goods to the Acropolis.

Ropemaker
Making the strong ropes which lifted the heavy blocks into place.

Painter
Decorating the carvings with bright colours.

Dyer
Using herbs and earth to dye Athene's robes.

Embroider
Embroidering the edges of Athene's long robe.

Weaver
Making clothes for the workmen and a robe for Athene.

Which of these jobs would you have liked to do? _____

_____

Why? _____

_____

_____

Greek Writing

The people in Ancient Greece wrote many books. They used a different alphabet from ours. Modern Greek is based on this alphabet.

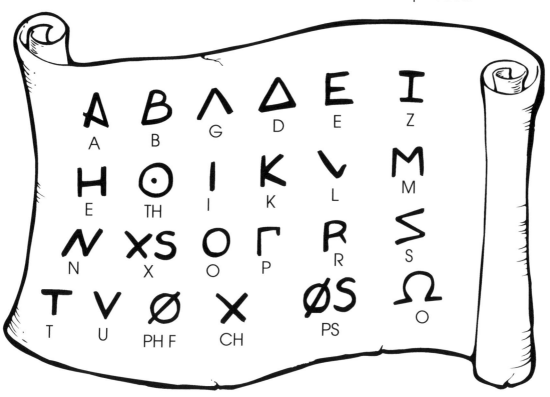

1. Using these letters can you write the name of your school?

_____

2. Can you translate this sentence? (Note: not all modern letters are included in the Greek alphabet.)

ΛΘΕΝS IS ΘΕ ΚΛΓΙΤΛV ΟØ ΜΩΔΕRΝ ΛRΕΕSΕ.

_____

_____

3. Make some sentences using Ancient Greek for your friends to translate.

_____

_____

_____

reek Words

Here are some Greek words and their meaning.

Polys = many	**Teles** = far off	**Peri** = around
Micros = small	**Techne** = skill	**Phone** = voice
Metry = measuring	**Graphy** = writing about	

Look at these prefixes.

Can you make a word we use in English from each? Maybe you know more than one.

poly_____   micro_____   tele_____

peri_____   techn_____   tele_____

Now use these suffixes.

_____phone   _____metry   _____graphy

_____phone   _____metry   _____graphy

_____phone   _____metry   _____graphy

Here are some Greek words for numbers.

Duo = Two	**Treis** = three	**Pente** = five
Hex = six	**Octo** = eight	**Deca** = ten

How many words can you think of which come from these Greek words?

_____

_____

_____

The Olympic Games

The Olympic games were held every four years at Olympia. They were held in honour of the god Zeus. Men came from all over Greece to participate.

Can you match the pictures with each event?

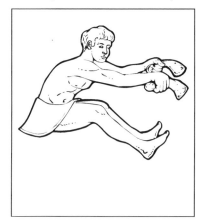  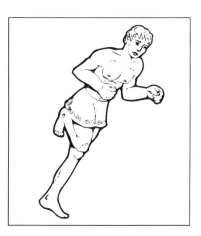

| Running | Javelin | Discus | Wrestling | Long Jump |

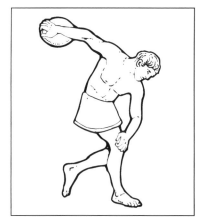 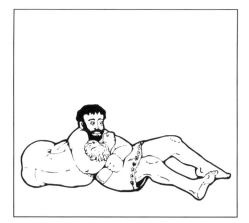

There was an event called the pentathlon in Ancient Greece.

There were _____ events completed in one afternoon.

Which events do you think were part of it. _____

Are any of these events still held in the modern Olympic Games? _____

_____

Do you know which ones? _____

Is there a pentathlon today? _____ Is it the same? _____

reek Gods and Goddesses

Can you match the speech bubbles to the pictures of these gods and goddesses?

Demeter

I am the goddess of love and beauty. My son is called Eros, he shoots arrows at people.

I am the King of the gods and ruler of the sky. I live on Mount Olympus.

Poseidon

Athena

I am the goddess of wisdom. Athens is named after me and the Parthenon was built for me.

I am the god of the sun. I am also the patron of music and the arts.

Zeus

Aphrodite

I am the god of the sea. I am a brother of Zeus.

I am the goddess of the harvest and the seasons. I am a sister of Zeus.

Apollo

The Story of the Seasons

Here is the Ancient Greek story telling how the seasons came about.

Can you put the illustrations in order?

Hades was the god of the underworld. He wanted a wife, but couldn't find one.

Persephone was the daughter of the goddess Demeter. She helped her mother sowing the seeds and picking the flowers.

One day Hades comes from the underworld and sees Persephone. He decides to take her to the underworld to be his wife. As Persephone crosses the River Styx she drops some flowers into the water.

Demeter is very unhappy without her daughter, but she cannot find her anywhere. Then she finds the flowers in the river flowing out of the underworld.

She goes to Zeus and asks him to tell Hades to give her back her daughter.

Persephone is very unhappy in the underworld. She will not eat anything. But she gets so hungry she eats six of the twelve pomegranate seeds.

Zeus sends Hermes to ask for Persephone to come back. She can come back if she has eaten nothing.

Zeus decides that because she has only eaten 6 of the 12 seeds she can spend six months in the underworld with Hades and six months with her mother.

Therefore when she is in the underworld Demeter is unhappy and we have autumn and winter, but when she is with her mother we have spring and summer.

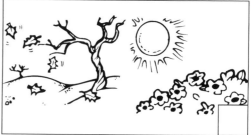

Greek Heroes

See if you can find the names of some famous heroes of Greek stories in the word grid.

| Jason | Odysseus | Paris | Theseus |
| Herakles | Perseus | Bellerophon |

There are drawings of them around the page.
You might like to find out more about each one and read the story.

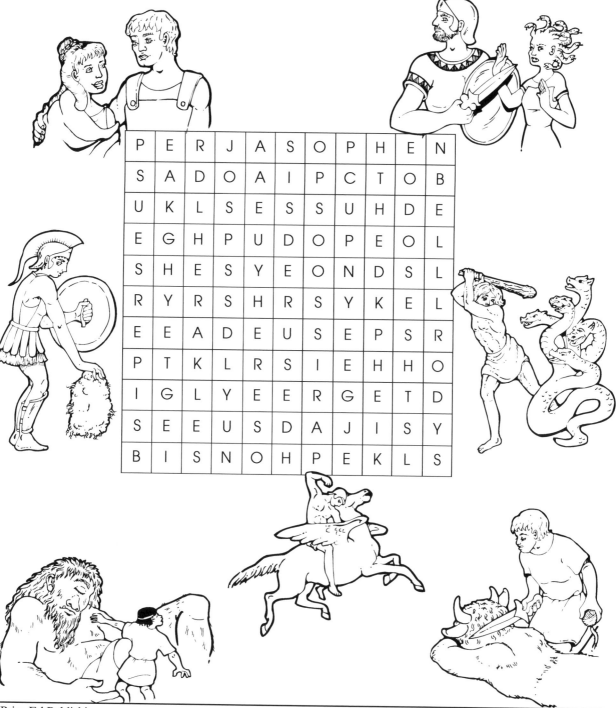

P	E	R	J	A	S	O	P	H	E	N
S	A	D	O	A	I	P	C	T	O	B
U	K	L	S	E	S	S	U	H	D	E
E	G	H	P	U	D	O	P	E	O	L
S	H	E	S	Y	E	O	N	D	S	L
R	Y	R	S	H	R	S	Y	K	E	L
E	E	A	D	E	U	S	E	P	S	R
P	T	K	L	R	S	I	E	H	H	O
I	G	L	Y	E	E	R	G	E	T	D
S	E	E	U	S	D	A	J	I	S	Y
B	I	S	N	O	H	P	E	K	L	S

reek Artefacts

Here are some Ancient Greek artefacts which have been found.

Can you complete the table saying what the find might have been used for and by whom?

Find	Used for	Used by
Urn		
Toga		
Sandal		
Coin		
Mask		
Lyre		
Drinking cup		
Pot for oil		

ncient Egypt

Colour the seas and the river blue. Shade the banks of the Nile green.
Shade the rest of the map a sandy colour for desert.

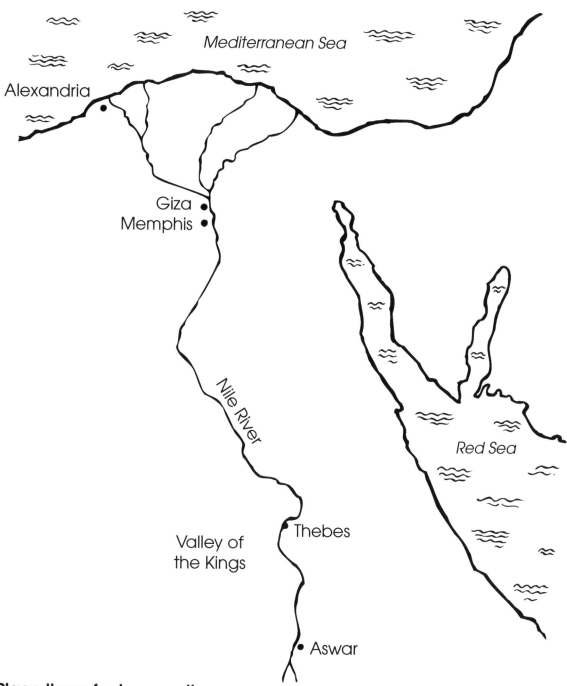

Place these features on the map.

1. Draw in some pyramids and the Sphinx on the west bank of the Nile near Giza.
2. Cairo is the present capital of Egypt.
   Mark it on the map near the Nile delta.
3. In 1971 a dam was finished at Aswan. Mark it on the map.

ncient Egypt Timelines

We can divide Ancient Egypt into five main periods of time.

Can you match each period with what happened during that period?

3100 BC Archaic Period	Egypt conquered Nubia.
2700 BC Old Kingdom	 Rameses II and Tutankhamun were pharaohs at this time.
2040 BC Middle Kingdom	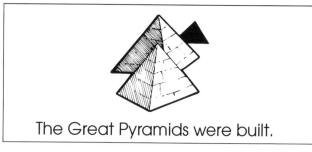 King Menes was the first ruler of Egypt.
1570 BC New Kingdom	The Great Pyramids were built.
1085 BC Late Period	 Several armies from other countries invaded Egypt.

Dates decrease when they are BC. Can you find out what BC means?

B _____   C _____

owerful People

Fill in the missing words.

Cut out the pictures and paste them beside the correct description.

The _____ was the most important person in

Egypt. He owned all the land and wealth. The people

thought he was a _____. Occasionally the

Pharaoh was a _____.

The person who helped the Pharaoh was called a

_____. He was the chief judge and in

charge of the _____.

People who could write were called _____.

They did not have to pay any _____, they

collected them from other people.

_____ and _____ looked after

the temples. They were in charge of worshipping the

gods and _____.

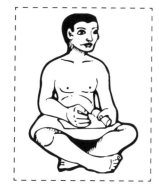   

ℬorking People in Egypt

Most people in Ancient Egypt worked very hard. They looked after the livestock and grew the crops. They also made things from metal, stone and wood. During the flood season, they couldn't work in the fields, so they were expected to help build the pyramids and other great monuments.

Can you match the pictures with the occupations?

making bricks

harvesting corn

making a wooden cabinet

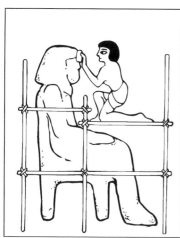

building pyramids

making wine

breaking stones to make statues

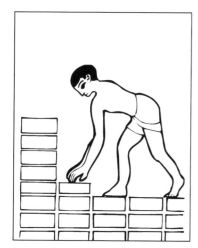

ℱamous Sites in Egypt

Egypt is famous for the ancient sites and monuments which we can still see today.

Can you name these sites?

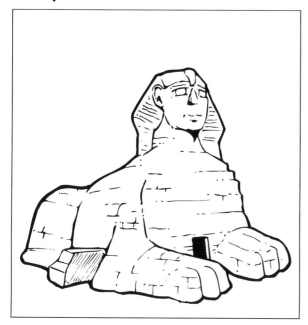

The _____

It is half lion and half human. It was built to guard the tombs.

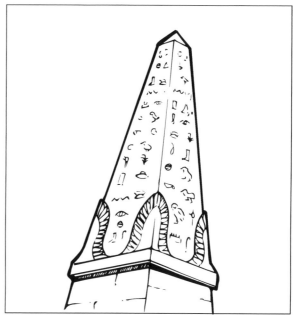

An _____

This tall, stone pillar has hieroglyphic writing carved on it.

The _____

These were built from stone blocks. They were used as tombs for some powerful Pharaohs.

A _____

This building had a magnificent statue of Rameses II. He was Pharaoh for 67 years.

Egyptian Writing

The Ancient Egyptians used pictures as we would use letters. They are called Hieroglyphs. There were more than 700 pictures, or signs to learn. Most people did not learn to read and write, those who did were called scribes.

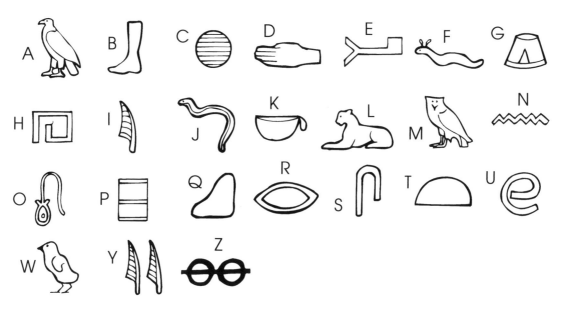

Use the code here to write your name in hieroglyphs.

_____

If you are a girl, draw this sign after your name.

If you are a boy, draw this sign after your name.

1. Exchange a message with a friend using hieroglyphs.

    _____

    _____

    _____

2. Decode the message you receive using the code.

    _____

    _____

    _____

# Entertainment

Answer these questions about Ancient Egypt. True or false?

Children's toys were made of plastic.

T	F

Ancient Egyptians liked to wear jewellery.

T	F

Both men and women wore make-up.

T	F

Dancers and acrobats performed at banquets.

T	F

Ancient Egyptians enjoyed electronic music.

T	F

Ancient Egyptians didn't have a dice when playing board games.

T	F

Children sometimes went to the cinema.

T	F

Poor people had more time for fun than rich people.

T	F

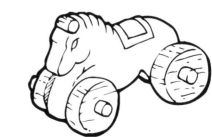

Farming and **H**unting

Look at these illustrations taken from wall paintings.

Match the statement to the correct pictures.

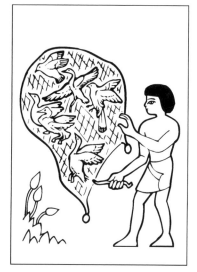

> The worker is winnowing by throwing grain into the air with scoops.

> The workers used oxen to pull the ploughs.

> The workers are harvesting the grain with sickles.

> The grain is stored in the granary.

> The worker is picking grapes.

> The worker is trapping birds in a net.

ood

Corn was one of the crops grown and harvested on the banks of the Nile river. It was used to make bread, cakes and biscuits.

Look at the other foods Ancient Egyptians ate and sort them into the correct sets.

The Ancient Egyptians grew these along the banks of the Nile River	
The Ancient Egyptians caught these in and around the Nile River	
The Ancient Egyptians looked after animals to produce these.	

Fish

Figs

Water birds

Meat

Grapes

Dates

Vegetables

Melon

Milk

Corn

Egyptian Gods and Goddesses

Can you match the speech bubbles to the pictures of these gods and goddesses?

Horus

> I am the god of children. I like music and dancing.

Bes

> Everyone will worship me. I am the King of the gods.

> I am the King of the Dead. I will decide whether you enter paradise.

Amon Ra

> I will take you to the scales where your heart will be weighed. I have the head of a jackal.

Osiris

Hathor

> I am the goddess of love. I will be there when babies are born, to protect them.

> If you pass the test, I will lead you into paradise. I have the head of a falcon.

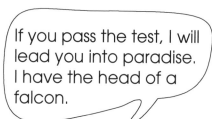

Anubis

ummification

The Ancient Egyptians denied death. They believed that the body was still important in the afterlife. Every Egyptian's body was preserved, but only the wealthy people had their bodies mummified. They used special ointments and wax to stop the body from decaying.

Can you match these statements about the mummification of bodies, to the pictures?

The body was covered in oils and perfumes.

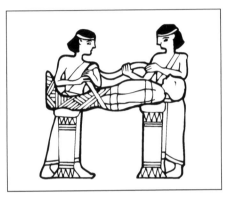

The internal organs were removed from the body and put into conopic jars.

The body was wrapped in linen bandages.

The Arabs call a preserved body a *mumiya,* and we have changed the word into *mummy.*

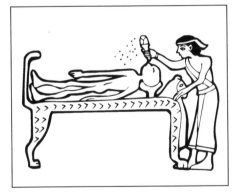

The body was dried out with sodium-carbonate.

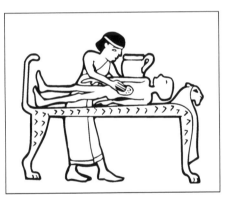

A mask was placed over the head.

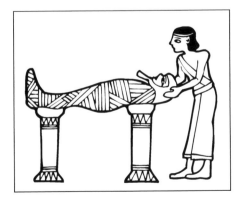

𝒫haraoh's Life After Death

When the body of a Pharaoh was buried, it was placed in his coffin, then in a sarcophagus then in the tomb. Many things were buried with him for his life after death.

Why do you think these items were buried in Tutankhamun's tomb? Write your reason under each picture.

Tutankhamun's Throne

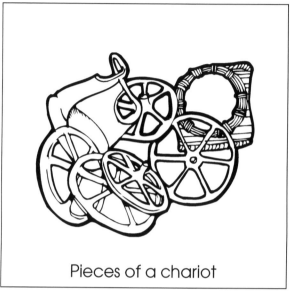

Pieces of a chariot

Dried flowers

Jewellery

Egyptian Artefacts

We know a lot about Ancient Egypt and how the Ancient Egyptians lived.

Can you think of one thing we may have learned from each of these objects?

Tutankhamun's death mask

Wall (tomb) painting

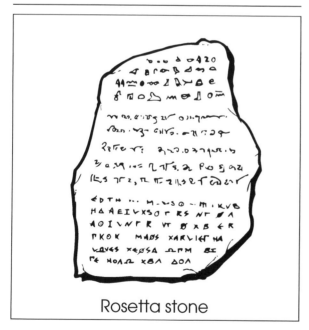

Rosetta stone

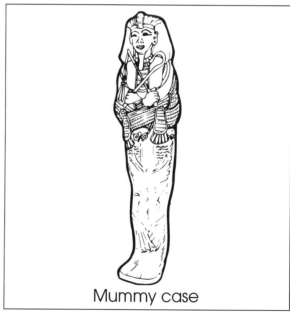

Mummy case

 # **W**ord **G**rid

1							
2							
3							
4							
5							
6							
7							
8							

1. The name for an Ancient Egyptian king.

2. A place where the Ancient Egyptians buried their kings.

3. A preserved body wrapped in cloth.

4. Egyptian paper was made from this.

5. A person who wrote hieroglyphs was called this.

6. This river flows through Egypt.

7. This machine was used to move water from the Nile to the fields.

8. A wall _____ can show us how the Ancient Egyptians lived.